Course Reports

Course __Royal Portrush – Northern Ireland__
Best holes __The 5th (White Rocks) + 14th__
(Calamity Corner) Two stunners amongst many!
Memories / comments __Holed out in 4 at 1st +__
felt like a pro. – not for long!
Calamity is a death or glory par 3 that
is wicked – the course is one of Colt's
best.

Course __Harlech – Royal St David's__
Best holes __15th – a long two-shotter with a blind__
2nd to cupped green. Last 4 holes agony for me
Memories / comments __Beautiful surroundings,__
romantic + brooding, with Harlech Castle
+ Snowdonia to take one's mind from
the purpose – to hit the ball straight!

Course __Rye – East Sussex (just)__
Best holes __The 4th is surely one of the__
finest two-shot holes in golf.
Memories / comments __A great iron-player's__
course, which is not my strength, though
I did manage to beat T.H. by 3 + 2.
Greens were slippery as eels.

Course __West Sussex (Pulborough)__
Best Holes __The 6th is a superb par 3 over a__
lily pond. 16th my favourite, 17th my disaster!
Memories / comments __Head + shoulders above__
most inland courses, with a charm +
subtlety that captivates. Delicious greens,
no bad holes. Like a miniature Pine Valley.

GOLFING
Record Book

'Quick, boy, a ferret.'

Edited by David White
with illustrations selected
from his collection

Ebury Press Stationery

Published in 1993 by Ebury Press Stationery
An imprint of Random House UK Ltd
20 Vauxhall Bridge Road
London SW1V 2SA

Copyright © Random House UK Ltd 1993

Editorial text and illustrations © David White 1993

All rights reserved. No part of this book may be reproduced in any form or
by any means without permission in writing from the publisher

Set in Elante

Printed in Singapore

Produced by Book Packaging and Marketing, Silverstone,
Northamptonshire, England

Designed by Robert Wheeler

Photography by Viccari Photography, Bolney, Sussex

Front cover illustration: Clement Flower,
"Harry Vardon, John Henry Taylor and James Braid, the great triumvirate".
Illustrated London News June 21st, 1913

Back cover illustration: early 20th century greetings card

Title page illustration: early 20th century postcard

ISBN 0 09 177504 3

Personal Details

Name _____

Address _____

_____ Post/zip code _____

Telephone (home) _____ (work) _____ Fax _____

Passport No _____ Driving Licence No _____

Doctor _____ Telephone _____

Dentist _____ Telephone _____

Golf / Country Club _____ Telephone _____

(Secretary) _____ (Clubhouse) _____ (Professional) _____

Glove size _____

Golf club details

Woods	Model	Shaft type	Shaft flex	Length	Swing weight	Loft	Lie
No 1 (Driver)							
No 2 (Brassie)							
No 3 (Spoon)							
Four wood							
Other							

Irons	Model	Shaft type	Shaft flex	Length	Swing weight	Loft	Lie
No 1							
No 2							
No 3							
No 4							
No 5							
No 6							
No 7							
No 8							
No 9							
Pitching wedge							
Sand wedge							

Putters _____

_____

Handicap _____ _____ _____

_____ _____ _____

Contents

Introduction

Golf is full of rich and wondrous memories, perhaps explaining why the game is so spell-binding. The conjuring up of grand or not so grand rounds played is the easiest of games and the most pleasurable. There are inspirational shots (for on a given day at a given hole, any golfer will play a shot or two that will outdo anything that Ballesteros, Faldo or Nicklaus can produce), or magical rounds played by one's heroes, for example Seve's sparkling 69 at St Andrews in 1984, to take The Open title by two strokes.

Golf is different from most other sports. It is played for the main part over acres of superb scenic beauty at a leisurely pace with a ball that won't move until you hit it! No one who plays tennis will find it possible to remember every shot or rally in a match, yet golfers not only remember every hole on the course (especially if they're playing well) but in the case of many top players, they can recall which club they used for each shot, able to give a blow by blow account.

But the memory of the event slowly dies unless it is recorded. Keeping records of favourite courses, or of that day when inspiration played a hand in your own game or that of your hero, will magnify those rounds of delight and the re-living will bring a warming glow on a winter's eve.

Additionally, the keeping of an individual eclectic (from the Greek *eklektikos* meaning choosing) score, i.e. the sum of a player's all-time personal best scores for each hole, is a fascination which will last a lifetime. The great journalist and broadcaster, Henry Longhurst, I believe was the first in 1959 to highlight the proper keeping of eclectic scores, recording that of Jim Morris, professional at Huntercombe, who at age 69 claimed an eclectic score of 313231233 (21) 331332332 (23) = 44. Within days, Leslie Taylor, son of the great John Henry Taylor, laid claim to an improvement with a personal best of 43 over Royal Mid-Surrey, including three 'aces'. According to the *Guinness Book of Records* those figures have tumbled rapidly down, the lowest ever recorded over a course of more than 6000 yards being by Jack McKinnon on the par-72, 6538 yard Capilano course in British Columbia, Canada. Compiled between 1937–64, it read 222122221 (16 out) and 212212223 (17 back) = 33.

The British record is 34 by John Harrowar 'Jock' Morrison at West Kilbride (par 70, 6348 yards) from 1951–78, comprising three aces, fourteen two's and one three.

There are no rules to this book and you alone will decide which round should be recorded. A round of 69 at St Andrews is great golf any time it is recorded, rain or shine, and by the same standards a 69 nett to take the Monthly Medal by a handful of shots is great golf. The execution may be different, but the feeling of elation will be just as real!

This simple record book will stimulate the recollection of memorable days and may also prove useful as a guide to both performance and course condition. Even if the compiler plays on only one course, the records will provide an assessment of his or her strengths or weaknesses, for no golf course ever plays exactly the same each time the player tees up. Tees are moved, the weather will dictate if the shot played last time with a wood is now a medium iron, the greens will alter in texture and speed, certainly slicker following the first cut of morning than when shadows lengthen and the evening fades. On that point, putting surfaces in Britain and Northern Europe comprise mainly native bent and fescue grasses, though often invaded by the weed grass *Poa annua*, especially on parkland courses. Speeds tend to be 'measured' in terms of slow, medium and fast. In warmer climes, especially in the United States where bent grasses are often used, speeds are usually measured by means of a 'stimpmeter', which records the distance a ball will roll from a set level. These are measured in feet, with 8–9 feet being medium and 10–12 feet as slick as putting on a polished table-top!

Record anything that takes your fancy: the flora, the fauna, the fun or the ill-fated. Remember always that this book is for dreaming. Play a great course just once and record it, or a great round when Old Man Par was urging you on, and you'll take that journey again and again whenever you turn the pages. Happy golfing.

David White

Round Reports

Course / Club _____ Date _____

Type of course (Links, etc.) _____

Length from medal tees _____ Club tees _____ Ladies tees _____

PAR _____ Standard scratch score (S.S.S.) _____

Weather conditions _____

Course conditions: tees _____ fairways _____ rough _____

bunkers _____ greens _____

Overall observations _____

Player/s 1 _____ handicap _____

2 _____ handicap _____

3 _____ handicap _____

4 _____ handicap _____

Method of play: match / medal / Stableford / other _____

Stroke analysis

1 ☐ 2 ☐ 3 ☐ 4 ☐ 5 ☐ 6 ☐ 7 ☐ 8 ☐ 9 ☐

Score at the turn ☐

10 ☐ 11 ☐ 12 ☐ 13 ☐ 14 ☐ 15 ☐ 16 ☐ 17 ☐ 18 ☐

total ☐

Putting analysis (putts per hole) 1 ☐ 2 ☐ 3 ☐ 4 ☐ 5 ☐ 6 ☐ 7 ☐

8 ☐ 9 ☐ 10 ☐ 11 ☐ 12 ☐ 13 ☐ 14 ☐ 15 ☐ 16 ☐ 17 ☐ 18 ☐

Match results _____ Gross score _____ Nett score _____

Memories _____

_____

_____

_____

_____

_____

Oilette Remarque illustrations by Lance Thackery.

THE GAME OF GOLF.
A Fine Stroke.

THE GAME OF GOLF.
A Match.

Round Reports

Course / Club _____ Date _____

Type of course (Links, etc.) _____

Length from medal tees _____ Club tees _____ Ladies tees _____

PAR _____ Standard scratch score (S.S.S.) _____

Weather conditions _____

_____

Course conditions: tees _____ fairways _____ rough _____

bunkers _____ greens _____

Overall observations _____

_____

Player/s 1 _____ handicap _____

2 _____ handicap _____

3 _____ handicap _____

4 _____ handicap _____

Method of play: match / medal / Stableford / other _____

Stroke analysis

1 ☐ 2 ☐ 3 ☐ 4 ☐ 5 ☐ 6 ☐ 7 ☐ 8 ☐ 9 ☐

Score at the turn ☐

10 ☐ 11 ☐ 12 ☐ 13 ☐ 14 ☐ 15 ☐ 16 ☐ 17 ☐ 18 ☐

total ☐

Putting analysis (putts per hole) 1 ☐ 2 ☐ 3 ☐ 4 ☐ 5 ☐ 6 ☐ 7 ☐

8 ☐ 9 ☐ 10 ☐ 11 ☐ 12 ☐ 13 ☐ 14 ☐ 15 ☐ 16 ☐ 17 ☐ 18 ☐

Match results _____ Gross score _____ Nett score _____

Memories _____

_____

_____

_____

_____

Score Card/Press Clippings/Notes

Round Reports

Course / Club _____ Date _____

Type of course (Links, etc.) _____

Length from medal tees _____ Club tees _____ Ladies tees _____

PAR _____ Standard scratch score (S.S.S.) _____

Weather conditions _____

_____

Course conditions: tees _____ fairways _____ rough _____

bunkers _____ greens _____

Overall observations _____

_____

_____

Player/s 1 _____ handicap _____

2 _____ handicap _____

3 _____ handicap _____

4 _____ handicap _____

Method of play: match / medal / Stableford / other _____

Stroke analysis

1 ☐ 2 ☐ 3 ☐ 4 ☐ 5 ☐ 6 ☐ 7 ☐ 8 ☐ 9 ☐

Score at the turn ☐

10 ☐ 11 ☐ 12 ☐ 13 ☐ 14 ☐ 15 ☐ 16 ☐ 17 ☐ 18 ☐

total ☐

Putting analysis (putts per hole) 1 ☐ 2 ☐ 3 ☐ 4 ☐ 5 ☐ 6 ☐ 7 ☐

8 ☐ 9 ☐ 10 ☐ 11 ☐ 12 ☐ 13 ☐ 14 ☐ 15 ☐ 16 ☐ 17 ☐ 18 ☐

Match results _____ Gross score _____ Nett score _____

Memories _____

_____

_____

_____

_____

_____

Pencil drawings by Frank Reynolds.

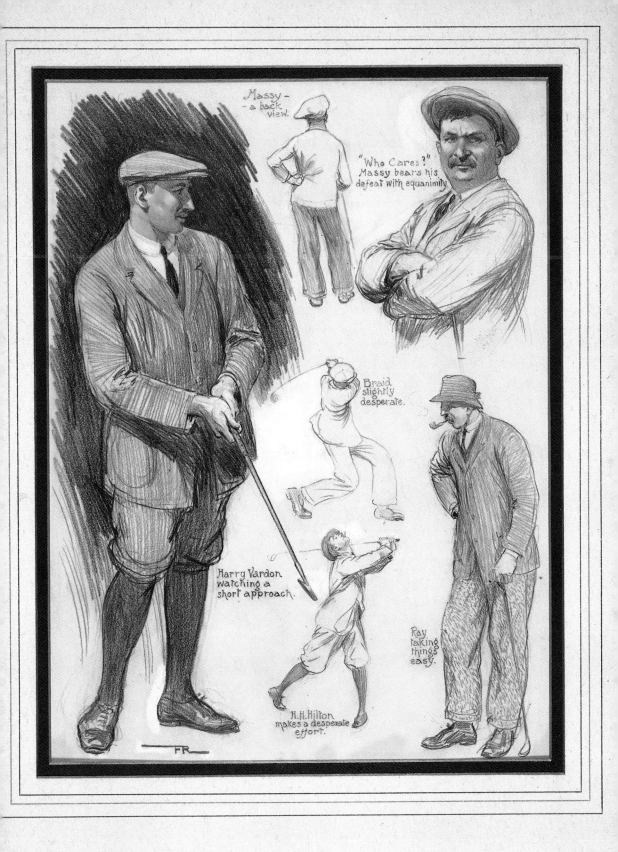

Massy -
- a back view.

"Who Cares?"
Massy bears his
defeat with equanimity.

Braid
slightly
desperate.

Harry Vardon
watching a
short approach.

H. H. Hilton
makes a desperate
effort.

Ray
taking
things
easy.

F R

Round Reports

Course / Club _____ Date _____

Type of course (Links, etc.) _____

Length from medal tees _____ Club tees _____ Ladies tees _____

PAR _____ Standard scratch score (S.S.S.) _____

Weather conditions _____

_____

Course conditions: tees _____ fairways _____ rough _____

bunkers _____ greens _____

Overall observations _____

_____

_____

Player/s 1 _____ handicap _____

2 _____ handicap _____

3 _____ handicap _____

4 _____ handicap _____

Method of play: match / medal / Stableford / other _____

Stroke analysis

1 ☐ 2 ☐ 3 ☐ 4 ☐ 5 ☐ 6 ☐ 7 ☐ 8 ☐ 9 ☐

Score at the turn ☐

10 ☐ 11 ☐ 12 ☐ 13 ☐ 14 ☐ 15 ☐ 16 ☐ 17 ☐ 18 ☐

total ☐

Putting analysis (putts per hole) 1 ☐ 2 ☐ 3 ☐ 4 ☐ 5 ☐ 6 ☐ 7 ☐

8 ☐ 9 ☐ 10 ☐ 11 ☐ 12 ☐ 13 ☐ 14 ☐ 15 ☐ 16 ☐ 17 ☐ 18 ☐

Match results _____ Gross score _____ Nett score _____

Memories _____

_____

_____

_____

_____

_____

Score Card/Press Clippings/Notes

Round Reports

Course / Club _____ Date _____

Type of course (Links, etc.) _____

Length from medal tees _____ Club tees _____ Ladies tees _____

PAR _____ Standard scratch score (S.S.S.) _____

Weather conditions _____

_____

Course conditions: tees _____ fairways _____ rough _____

bunkers _____ greens _____

Overall observations _____

_____

_____

Player/s 1 _____ handicap _____

2 _____ handicap _____

3 _____ handicap _____

4 _____ handicap _____

Method of play: match / medal / Stableford / other _____

Stroke analysis

1 ☐ 2 ☐ 3 ☐ 4 ☐ 5 ☐ 6 ☐ 7 ☐ 8 ☐ 9 ☐

Score at the turn ☐

10 ☐ 11 ☐ 12 ☐ 13 ☐ 14 ☐ 15 ☐ 16 ☐ 17 ☐ 18 ☐

total ☐

Putting analysis (putts per hole) 1 ☐ 2 ☐ 3 ☐ 4 ☐ 5 ☐ 6 ☐ 7 ☐

8 ☐ 9 ☐ 10 ☐ 11 ☐ 12 ☐ 13 ☐ 14 ☐ 15 ☐ 16 ☐ 17 ☐ 18 ☐

Match results _____ Gross score _____ Nett score _____

Memories _____

_____

_____

_____

_____

_____

Royal golfers at Sandringham, still a Royal residence.

The Children of
T.R.H. the Prince & Princess of Wales.
York Cottage, Sandringham.

Score Card/Press Clippings/Notes

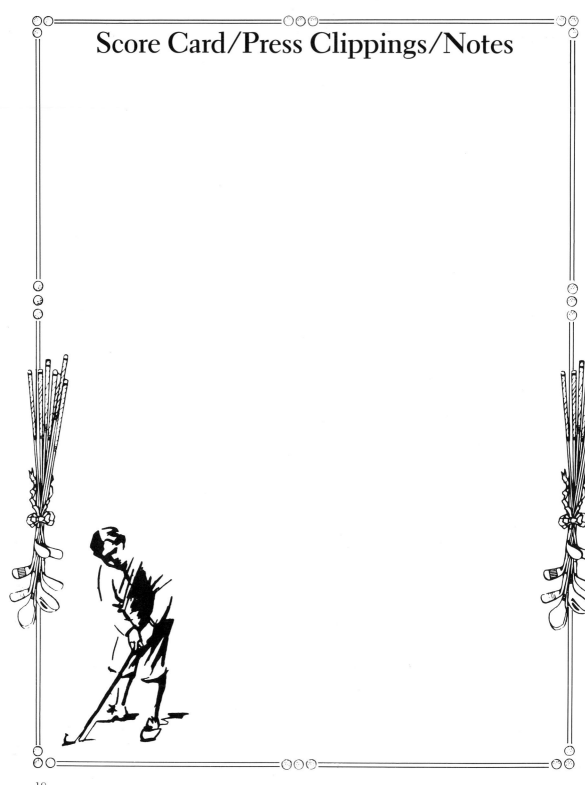

Round Reports

Course / Club _____ Date _____

Type of course (Links, etc.) _____

Length from medal tees _____ Club tees _____ Ladies tees _____

PAR _____ Standard scratch score (S.S.S.) _____

Weather conditions _____

_____

Course conditions: tees _____ fairways _____ rough _____

bunkers _____ greens _____

Overall observations _____

_____

_____

Player/s 1 _____ handicap _____

2 _____ handicap _____

3 _____ handicap _____

4 _____ handicap _____

Method of play: match / medal / Stableford / other _____

Stroke analysis

1 ☐ 2 ☐ 3 ☐ 4 ☐ 5 ☐ 6 ☐ 7 ☐ 8 ☐ 9 ☐

Score at the turn ☐

10 ☐ 11 ☐ 12 ☐ 13 ☐ 14 ☐ 15 ☐ 16 ☐ 17 ☐ 18 ☐

total ☐

Putting analysis (putts per hole) 1 ☐ 2 ☐ 3 ☐ 4 ☐ 5 ☐ 6 ☐ 7 ☐

8 ☐ 9 ☐ 10 ☐ 11 ☐ 12 ☐ 13 ☐ 14 ☐ 15 ☐ 16 ☐ 17 ☐ 18 ☐

Match results _____ Gross score _____ Nett score _____

Memories _____

_____

_____

_____

_____

_____

_____

Round Reports

Course / Club _____ Date _____

Type of course (Links, etc.) _____

Length from medal tees _____ Club tees _____ Ladies tees _____

PAR _____ Standard scratch score (S.S.S.) _____

Weather conditions _____

_____

Course conditions: tees _____ fairways _____ rough _____

bunkers _____ greens _____

Overall observations _____

_____

_____

Player/s 1 _____ handicap _____

2 _____ handicap _____

3 _____ handicap _____

4 _____ handicap _____

Method of play: match / medal / Stableford / other _____

Stroke analysis

1 ☐ 2 ☐ 3 ☐ 4 ☐ 5 ☐ 6 ☐ 7 ☐ 8 ☐ 9 ☐

Score at the turn ☐

10 ☐ 11 ☐ 12 ☐ 13 ☐ 14 ☐ 15 ☐ 16 ☐ 17 ☐ 18 ☐

total ☐

Putting analysis (putts per hole) 1 ☐ 2 ☐ 3 ☐ 4 ☐ 5 ☐ 6 ☐ 7 ☐

8 ☐ 9 ☐ 10 ☐ 11 ☐ 12 ☐ 13 ☐ 14 ☐ 15 ☐ 16 ☐ 17 ☐ 18 ☐

Match results _____ Gross score _____ Nett score _____

Memories _____

_____

_____

_____

_____

_____

The beauties of nature – by Frank Reynolds.

Round Reports

Course / Club _____ Date _____

Type of course (Links, etc.) _____

Length from medal tees _____ Club tees _____ Ladies tees _____

PAR _____ Standard scratch score (S.S.S.) _____

Weather conditions _____
_____

Course conditions: tees _____ fairways _____ rough _____

bunkers _____ greens _____

Overall observations _____
_____
_____

Player/s 1 _____ handicap _____

2 _____ handicap _____

3 _____ handicap _____

4 _____ handicap _____

Method of play: match / medal / Stableford / other _____

Stroke analysis

1 ☐ 2 ☐ 3 ☐ 4 ☐ 5 ☐ 6 ☐ 7 ☐ 8 ☐ 9 ☐

Score at the turn ☐

10 ☐ 11 ☐ 12 ☐ 13 ☐ 14 ☐ 15 ☐ 16 ☐ 17 ☐ 18 ☐

total ☐

Putting analysis (putts per hole) 1 ☐ 2 ☐ 3 ☐ 4 ☐ 5 ☐ 6 ☐ 7 ☐

8 ☐ 9 ☐ 10 ☐ 11 ☐ 12 ☐ 13 ☐ 14 ☐ 15 ☐ 16 ☐ 17 ☐ 18 ☐

Match results _____ Gross score _____ Nett score _____

Memories _____
_____
_____
_____
_____
_____

Score Card/Press Clippings/Notes

Round Reports

Course / Club _____ Date _____

Type of course (Links, etc.) _____

Length from medal tees _____ Club tees _____ Ladies tees _____

PAR _____ Standard scratch score (S.S.S.) _____

Weather conditions _____

_____

Course conditions: tees _____ fairways _____ rough _____

bunkers _____ greens _____

Overall observations _____

_____

_____

Player/s   1 _____ handicap _____

2 _____ handicap _____

3 _____ handicap _____

4 _____ handicap _____

Method of play: match / medal / Stableford / other _____

Stroke analysis

1 ☐ 2 ☐ 3 ☐ 4 ☐ 5 ☐ 6 ☐ 7 ☐ 8 ☐ 9 ☐

Score at the turn ☐

10 ☐ 11 ☐ 12 ☐ 13 ☐ 14 ☐ 15 ☐ 16 ☐ 17 ☐ 18 ☐

total ☐

Putting analysis (putts per hole) 1 ☐ 2 ☐ 3 ☐ 4 ☐ 5 ☐ 6 ☐ 7 ☐

8 ☐ 9 ☐ 10 ☐ 11 ☐ 12 ☐ 13 ☐ 14 ☐ 15 ☐ 16 ☐ 17 ☐ 18 ☐

Match results _____ Gross score _____ Nett score _____

Memories _____

_____

_____

_____

_____

_____

A classic book cover from a gentler age, the 1890s.

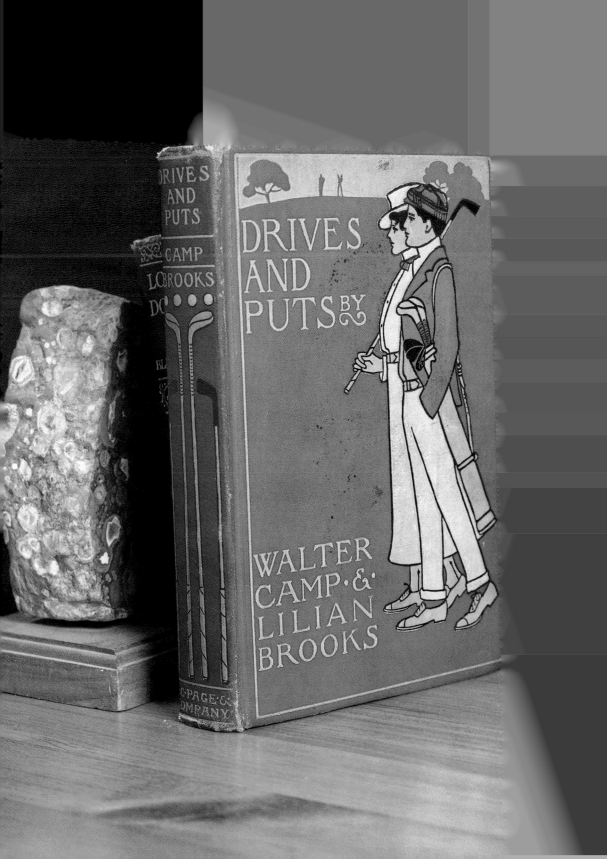

Score Card/Press Clippings/Notes

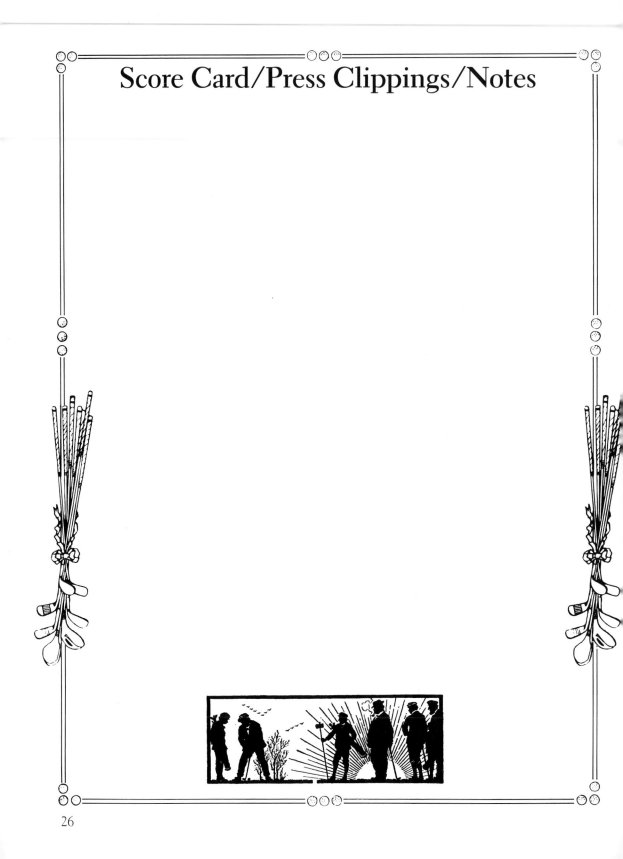

Round Reports

Course / Club _____ Date _____

Type of course (Links, etc.) _____

Length from medal tees _____ Club tees _____ Ladies tees _____

PAR _____ Standard scratch score (S.S.S.) _____

Weather conditions _____

_____

Course conditions: tees _____ fairways _____ rough _____

bunkers _____ greens _____

Overall observations _____

_____

_____

Player/s 1 _____ handicap _____

2 _____ handicap _____

3 _____ handicap _____

4 _____ handicap _____

Method of play: match / medal / Stableford / other _____

Stroke analysis

1 ☐ 2 ☐ 3 ☐ 4 ☐ 5 ☐ 6 ☐ 7 ☐ 8 ☐ 9 ☐

Score at the turn ☐

10 ☐ 11 ☐ 12 ☐ 13 ☐ 14 ☐ 15 ☐ 16 ☐ 17 ☐ 18 ☐

total ☐

Putting analysis (putts per hole) 1 ☐ 2 ☐ 3 ☐ 4 ☐ 5 ☐ 6 ☐ 7 ☐

8 ☐ 9 ☐ 10 ☐ 11 ☐ 12 ☐ 13 ☐ 14 ☐ 15 ☐ 16 ☐ 17 ☐ 18 ☐

Match results _____ Gross score _____ Nett score _____

Memories _____

_____

_____

_____

_____

_____

Round Reports

Course / Club _____ Date _____

Type of course (Links, etc.) _____

Length from medal tees _____ Club tees _____ Ladies tees _____

PAR _____ Standard scratch score (S.S.S.) _____

Weather conditions _____
_____

Course conditions: tees _____ fairways _____ rough _____

bunkers _____ greens _____

Overall observations _____
_____
_____

Player/s 1 _____ handicap _____

2 _____ handicap _____

3 _____ handicap _____

4 _____ handicap _____

Method of play: match / medal / Stableford / other _____

Stroke analysis

1 ☐ 2 ☐ 3 ☐ 4 ☐ 5 ☐ 6 ☐ 7 ☐ 8 ☐ 9 ☐

Score at the turn ☐

10 ☐ 11 ☐ 12 ☐ 13 ☐ 14 ☐ 15 ☐ 16 ☐ 17 ☐ 18 ☐

total ☐

Putting analysis (putts per hole) 1 ☐ 2 ☐ 3 ☐ 4 ☐ 5 ☐ 6 ☐ 7 ☐
8 ☐ 9 ☐ 10 ☐ 11 ☐ 12 ☐ 13 ☐ 14 ☐ 15 ☐ 16 ☐ 17 ☐ 18 ☐

Match results _____ Gross score _____ Nett score _____

Memories _____
_____
_____
_____
_____
_____

1.—A Short Putt.

3.—Keep your eye on the ball.

6.—A Drive. "Where is it."

7.—Missed the globe.

10.—A Bad Lie.

15.—A Stymie.

17.—The Tee Shot.

18.—"Delights of a Bunker."

23.—A Duffer's Stroke.

34.—Dormy.

36.—The Mystery of a Bunker. "How many's that?"

37.—A Long Putt.

Round Reports

Course / Club _____ Date _____

Type of course (Links, etc.) _____

Length from medal tees _____ Club tees _____ Ladies tees _____

PAR _____ Standard scratch score (S.S.S.) _____

Weather conditions _____

_____

Course conditions: tees _____ fairways _____ rough _____

bunkers _____ greens _____

Overall observations _____

_____

_____

Player/s 1 _____ handicap _____

2 _____ handicap _____

3 _____ handicap _____

4 _____ handicap _____

Method of play: match / medal / Stableford / other _____

Stroke analysis

1 ☐ 2 ☐ 3 ☐ 4 ☐ 5 ☐ 6 ☐ 7 ☐ 8 ☐ 9 ☐

Score at the turn ☐

10 ☐ 11 ☐ 12 ☐ 13 ☐ 14 ☐ 15 ☐ 16 ☐ 17 ☐ 18 ☐

total ☐

Putting analysis (putts per hole) 1 ☐ 2 ☐ 3 ☐ 4 ☐ 5 ☐ 6 ☐ 7 ☐

8 ☐ 9 ☐ 10 ☐ 11 ☐ 12 ☐ 13 ☐ 14 ☐ 15 ☐ 16 ☐ 17 ☐ 18 ☐

Match results _____ Gross score _____ Nett score _____

Memories _____

_____

_____

_____

_____

_____

Score Card/Press Clippings/Notes

Round Reports

Course / Club _____ Date _____

Type of course (Links, etc.) _____

Length from medal tees _____ Club tees _____ Ladies tees _____

PAR _____ Standard scratch score (S.S.S.) _____

Weather conditions _____

_____

Course conditions: tees _____ fairways _____ rough _____

bunkers _____ greens _____

Overall observations _____

_____

_____

Player/s 1 _____ handicap _____

2 _____ handicap _____

3 _____ handicap _____

4 _____ handicap _____

Method of play: match / medal / Stableford / other _____

Stroke analysis

1 ☐ 2 ☐ 3 ☐ 4 ☐ 5 ☐ 6 ☐ 7 ☐ 8 ☐ 9 ☐

Score at the turn ☐

10 ☐ 11 ☐ 12 ☐ 13 ☐ 14 ☐ 15 ☐ 16 ☐ 17 ☐ 18 ☐

total ☐

Putting analysis (putts per hole) 1 ☐ 2 ☐ 3 ☐ 4 ☐ 5 ☐ 6 ☐ 7 ☐

8 ☐ 9 ☐ 10 ☐ 11 ☐ 12 ☐ 13 ☐ 14 ☐ 15 ☐ 16 ☐ 17 ☐ 18 ☐

Match results _____ Gross score _____ Nett score _____

Memories _____

_____

_____

_____

_____

_____

An alternative to suicide!

THE GOLFICIDE

Round Reports

Course / Club _____ Date _____

Type of course (Links, etc.) _____

Length from medal tees _____ Club tees _____ Ladies tees _____

PAR _____ Standard scratch score (S.S.S.) _____

Weather conditions _____

_____

Course conditions: tees _____ fairways _____ rough _____

bunkers _____ greens _____

Overall observations _____

_____

_____

Player/s 1 _____ handicap _____

2 _____ handicap _____

3 _____ handicap _____

4 _____ handicap _____

Method of play: match / medal / Stableford / other _____

Stroke analysis

1 ☐ 2 ☐ 3 ☐ 4 ☐ 5 ☐ 6 ☐ 7 ☐ 8 ☐ 9 ☐

Score at the turn ☐

10 ☐ 11 ☐ 12 ☐ 13 ☐ 14 ☐ 15 ☐ 16 ☐ 17 ☐ 18 ☐

total ☐

Putting analysis (putts per hole) 1 ☐ 2 ☐ 3 ☐ 4 ☐ 5 ☐ 6 ☐ 7 ☐

8 ☐ 9 ☐ 10 ☐ 11 ☐ 12 ☐ 13 ☐ 14 ☐ 15 ☐ 16 ☐ 17 ☐ 18 ☐

Match results _____ Gross score _____ Nett score _____

Memories _____

_____

_____

_____

_____

_____

Score Card/Press Clippings/Notes

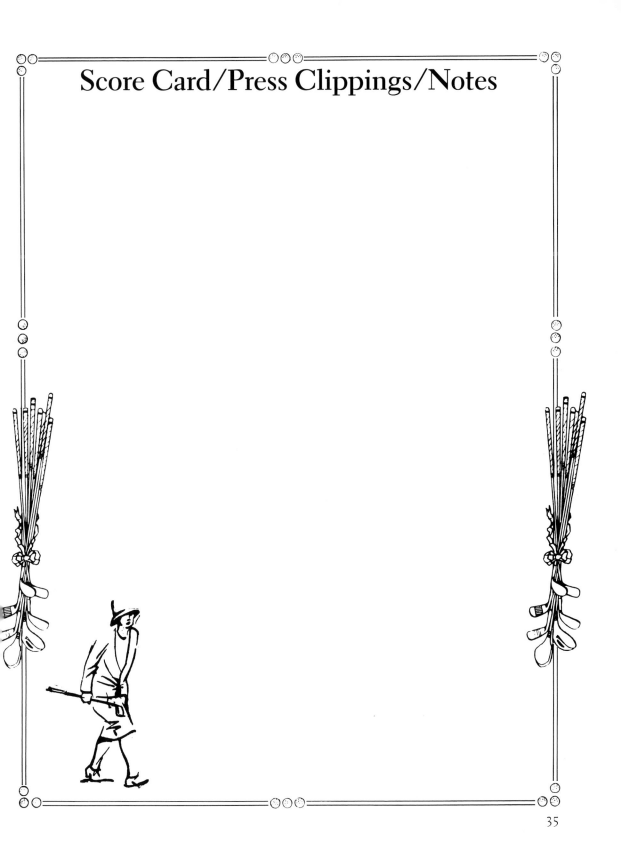

Round Reports

Course / Club _____ Date _____

Type of course (Links, etc.) _____

Length from medal tees _____ Club tees _____ Ladies tees _____

PAR _____ Standard scratch score (S.S.S.) _____

Weather conditions _____

_____

Course conditions: tees _____ fairways _____ rough _____

bunkers _____ greens _____

Overall observations _____

_____

_____

Player/s 1 _____ handicap _____

         2 _____ handicap _____

         3 _____ handicap _____

         4 _____ handicap _____

Method of play: match / medal / Stableford / other _____

Stroke analysis

    1 ☐   2 ☐   3 ☐   4 ☐   5 ☐   6 ☐   7 ☐   8 ☐   9 ☐

                           Score at the turn ☐

   10 ☐   11 ☐   12 ☐   13 ☐   14 ☐   15 ☐   16 ☐   17 ☐   18 ☐

                           total ☐

Putting analysis (putts per hole) 1 ☐   2 ☐   3 ☐   4 ☐   5 ☐   6 ☐   7 ☐

8 ☐   9 ☐   10 ☐   11 ☐   12 ☐   13 ☐   14 ☐   15 ☐   16 ☐   17 ☐   18 ☐

Match results _____ Gross score _____ Nett score _____

Memories _____

_____

_____

_____

_____

_____

By C. Dana Gibson. From "Snap-Shots." Copyright.

ADVICE TO CADDIES.—You will save time by keeping your eye on the ball, not on the player.

By C. Dana Gibson. From "Snap-Shots." Copyright.

GOLF IS NOT THE ONLY GAME ON EARTH.

Score Card/Press Clippings/Notes

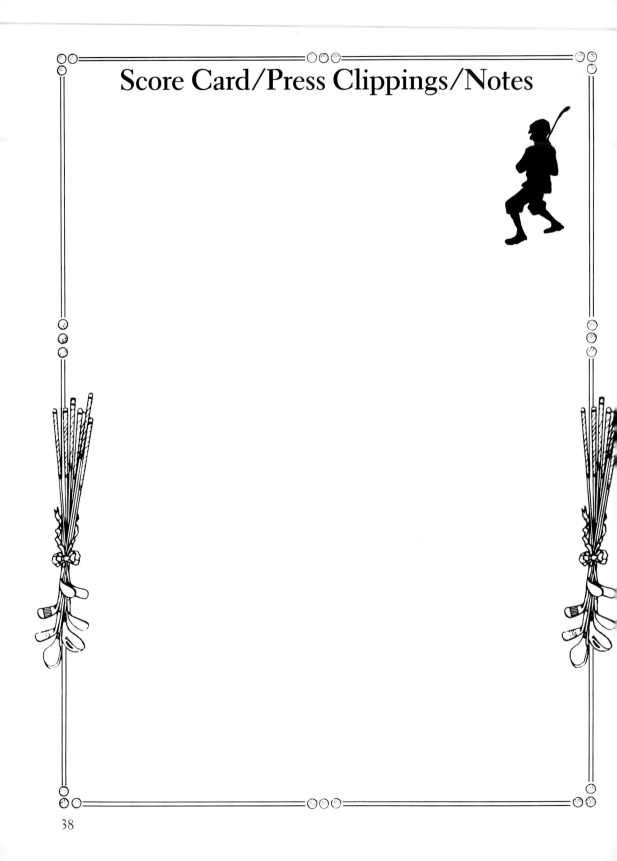

Round Reports

Course / Club _____ Date _____

Type of course (Links, etc.) _____

Length from medal tees _____ Club tees _____ Ladies tees _____

PAR _____ Standard scratch score (S.S.S.) _____

Weather conditions _____

_____

Course conditions: tees _____ fairways _____ rough _____

bunkers _____ greens _____

Overall observations _____

_____

_____

Player/s 1 _____ handicap _____

2 _____ handicap _____

3 _____ handicap _____

4 _____ handicap _____

Method of play: match / medal / Stableford / other _____

Stroke analysis

1 ☐ 2 ☐ 3 ☐ 4 ☐ 5 ☐ 6 ☐ 7 ☐ 8 ☐ 9 ☐

Score at the turn ☐

10 ☐ 11 ☐ 12 ☐ 13 ☐ 14 ☐ 15 ☐ 16 ☐ 17 ☐ 18 ☐

total ☐

Putting analysis (putts per hole) 1 ☐ 2 ☐ 3 ☐ 4 ☐ 5 ☐ 6 ☐ 7 ☐

8 ☐ 9 ☐ 10 ☐ 11 ☐ 12 ☐ 13 ☐ 14 ☐ 15 ☐ 16 ☐ 17 ☐ 18 ☐

Match results _____ Gross score _____ Nett score _____

Memories _____

_____

_____

_____

_____

_____

Round Reports

Course / Club _____ Date _____

Type of course (Links, etc.) _____

Length from medal tees _____ Club tees _____ Ladies tees _____

PAR _____ Standard scratch score (S.S.S.) _____

Weather conditions _____

_____

Course conditions: tees _____ fairways _____ rough _____

bunkers _____ greens _____

Overall observations _____

_____

_____

Player/s 1 _____ handicap _____

2 _____ handicap _____

3 _____ handicap _____

4 _____ handicap _____

Method of play: match / medal / Stableford / other _____

Stroke analysis

1 ☐ 2 ☐ 3 ☐ 4 ☐ 5 ☐ 6 ☐ 7 ☐ 8 ☐ 9 ☐

Score at the turn ☐

10 ☐ 11 ☐ 12 ☐ 13 ☐ 14 ☐ 15 ☐ 16 ☐ 17 ☐ 18 ☐

total ☐

Putting analysis (putts per hole) 1 ☐ 2 ☐ 3 ☐ 4 ☐ 5 ☐ 6 ☐ 7 ☐

8 ☐ 9 ☐ 10 ☐ 11 ☐ 12 ☐ 13 ☐ 14 ☐ 15 ☐ 16 ☐ 17 ☐ 18 ☐

Match results _____ Gross score _____ Nett score _____

Memories _____

_____

_____

_____

_____

_____

CHURCHMAN'S CIGARETTES

MISS JOYCE WETHERED

CHURCHMAN'S CIGARETTES

FRANCIS OUIMET

CHURCHMAN'S CIGARETTES

JAMES BRAID

CHURCHMAN'S CIGARETTES

BOBBY JONES

CHURCHMAN'S CIGARETTES

WALTER HAGEN

CHURCHMAN'S CIGARETTES

A. HERD

Round Reports

Course / Club _____ Date _____

Type of course (Links, etc.) _____

Length from medal tees _____ Club tees _____ Ladies tees _____

PAR _____ Standard scratch score (S.S.S.) _____

Weather conditions _____

_____

Course conditions: tees _____ fairways _____ rough _____

bunkers _____ greens _____

Overall observations _____

_____

Player/s 1 _____ handicap _____

2 _____ handicap _____

3 _____ handicap _____

4 _____ handicap _____

Method of play: match / medal / Stableford / other _____

Stroke analysis

1 □ 2 □ 3 □ 4 □ 5 □ 6 □ 7 □ 8 □ 9 □

Score at the turn □

10 □ 11 □ 12 □ 13 □ 14 □ 15 □ 16 □ 17 □ 18 □

total □

Putting analysis (putts per hole) 1 □ 2 □ 3 □ 4 □ 5 □ 6 □ 7 □

8 □ 9 □ 10 □ 11 □ 12 □ 13 □ 14 □ 15 □ 16 □ 17 □ 18 □

Match results _____ Gross score _____ Nett score _____

Memories _____

_____

_____

_____

_____

_____

Score Card/Press Clippings/Notes

Course / Club _____ Date _____

Type of course (Links, etc.) _____

Length from medal tees _____ Club tees _____ Ladies tees _____

PAR _____ Standard scratch score (S.S.S.) _____

Weather conditions _____

_____

Course conditions: tees _____ fairways _____ rough _____

bunkers _____ greens _____

Overall observations _____

_____

_____

Player/s 1 _____ handicap _____

        2 _____ handicap _____

        3 _____ handicap _____

        4 _____ handicap _____

Method of play: match / medal / Stableford / other _____

Stroke analysis

1 ☐ 2 ☐ 3 ☐ 4 ☐ 5 ☐ 6 ☐ 7 ☐ 8 ☐ 9 ☐

Score at the turn ☐

10 ☐ 11 ☐ 12 ☐ 13 ☐ 14 ☐ 15 ☐ 16 ☐ 17 ☐ 18 ☐

total ☐

Putting analysis (putts per hole) 1 ☐ 2 ☐ 3 ☐ 4 ☐ 5 ☐ 6 ☐ 7 ☐

8 ☐ 9 ☐ 10 ☐ 11 ☐ 12 ☐ 13 ☐ 14 ☐ 15 ☐ 16 ☐ 17 ☐ 18 ☐

Match results _____ Gross score _____ Nett score _____

Memories _____

_____

_____

_____

_____

_____

Score Card/Press Clippings/Notes

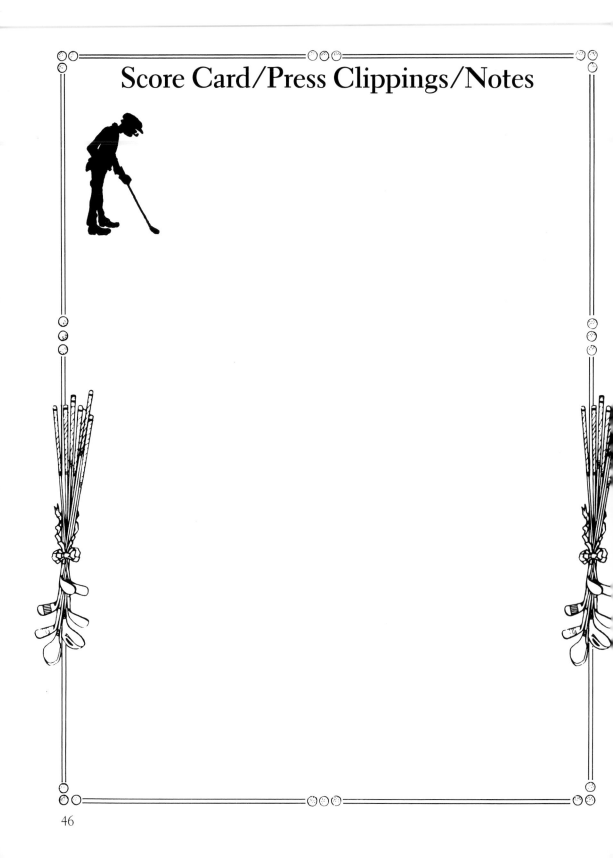

Round Reports

Course / Club _____ Date _____

Type of course (Links, etc.) _____

Length from medal tees _____ Club tees _____ Ladies tees _____

PAR _____ Standard scratch score (S.S.S.) _____

Weather conditions _____
_____

Course conditions: tees _____ fairways _____ rough _____

bunkers _____ greens _____

Overall observations _____
_____
_____

Player/s 1 _____ handicap _____

2 _____ handicap _____

3 _____ handicap _____

4 _____ handicap _____

Method of play: match / medal / Stableford / other _____

Stroke analysis

1 ☐ 2 ☐ 3 ☐ 4 ☐ 5 ☐ 6 ☐ 7 ☐ 8 ☐ 9 ☐

Score at the turn ☐

10 ☐ 11 ☐ 12 ☐ 13 ☐ 14 ☐ 15 ☐ 16 ☐ 17 ☐ 18 ☐

total ☐

Putting analysis (putts per hole) 1 ☐ 2 ☐ 3 ☐ 4 ☐ 5 ☐ 6 ☐ 7 ☐

8 ☐ 9 ☐ 10 ☐ 11 ☐ 12 ☐ 13 ☐ 14 ☐ 15 ☐ 16 ☐ 17 ☐ 18 ☐

Match results _____ Gross score _____ Nett score _____

Memories _____
_____
_____
_____
_____
_____
_____

Round Reports

Course / Club _____ Date _____

Type of course (Links, etc.) _____

Length from medal tees _____ Club tees _____ Ladies tees _____

PAR _____ Standard scratch score (S.S.S.) _____

Weather conditions _____

Course conditions: tees _____ fairways _____ rough _____

bunkers _____ greens _____

Overall observations _____

_____

_____

Player/s 1 _____ handicap _____

2 _____ handicap _____

3 _____ handicap _____

4 _____ handicap _____

Method of play: match / medal / Stableford / other _____

Stroke analysis

1 ☐ 2 ☐ 3 ☐ 4 ☐ 5 ☐ 6 ☐ 7 ☐ 8 ☐ 9 ☐

Score at the turn ☐

10 ☐ 11 ☐ 12 ☐ 13 ☐ 14 ☐ 15 ☐ 16 ☐ 17 ☐ 18 ☐

total ☐

Putting analysis (putts per hole) 1 ☐ 2 ☐ 3 ☐ 4 ☐ 5 ☐ 6 ☐ 7 ☐

8 ☐ 9 ☐ 10 ☐ 11 ☐ 12 ☐ 13 ☐ 14 ☐ 15 ☐ 16 ☐ 17 ☐ 18 ☐

Match results _____ Gross score _____ Nett score _____

Memories _____

_____

_____

_____

_____

_____

Then as now, the great players offer advice.

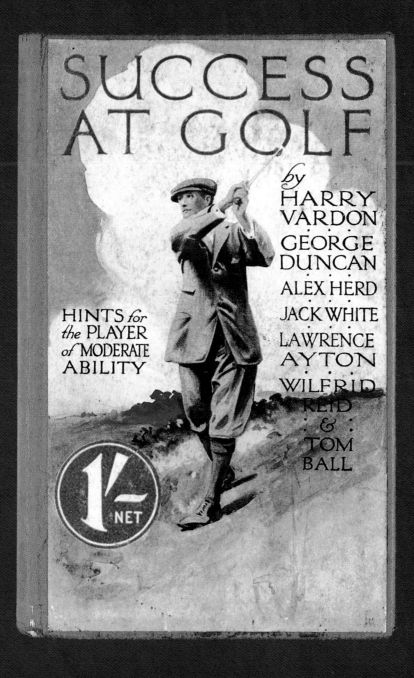

Round Reports

Course / Club _____ Date _____

Type of course (Links, etc.) _____

Length from medal tees _____ Club tees _____ Ladies tees _____

PAR _____ Standard scratch score (S.S.S.) _____

Weather conditions _____

_____

Course conditions: tees _____ fairways _____ rough _____

bunkers _____ greens _____

Overall observations _____

_____

_____

Player/s 1 _____ handicap _____

2 _____ handicap _____

3 _____ handicap _____

4 _____ handicap _____

Method of play: match / medal / Stableford / other _____

Stroke analysis

1 ☐ 2 ☐ 3 ☐ 4 ☐ 5 ☐ 6 ☐ 7 ☐ 8 ☐ 9 ☐

Score at the turn ☐

10 ☐ 11 ☐ 12 ☐ 13 ☐ 14 ☐ 15 ☐ 16 ☐ 17 ☐ 18 ☐

total ☐

Putting analysis (putts per hole) 1 ☐ 2 ☐ 3 ☐ 4 ☐ 5 ☐ 6 ☐ 7 ☐

8 ☐ 9 ☐ 10 ☐ 11 ☐ 12 ☐ 13 ☐ 14 ☐ 15 ☐ 16 ☐ 17 ☐ 18 ☐

Match results _____ Gross score _____ Nett score _____

Memories _____

_____

_____

_____

_____

Score Card/Press Clippings/Notes

Round Reports

Course / Club _____ Date _____

Type of course (Links, etc.) _____

Length from medal tees _____ Club tees _____ Ladies tees _____

PAR _____ Standard scratch score (S.S.S.) _____

Weather conditions _____

_____

Course conditions: tees _____ fairways _____ rough _____

bunkers _____ greens _____

Overall observations _____

_____

_____

Player/s 1 _____ handicap _____

2 _____ handicap _____

3 _____ handicap _____

4 _____ handicap _____

Method of play: match / medal / Stableford / other _____

Stroke analysis

1 ☐ 2 ☐ 3 ☐ 4 ☐ 5 ☐ 6 ☐ 7 ☐ 8 ☐ 9 ☐

Score at the turn ☐

10 ☐ 11 ☐ 12 ☐ 13 ☐ 14 ☐ 15 ☐ 16 ☐ 17 ☐ 18 ☐

total ☐

Putting analysis (putts per hole) 1 ☐ 2 ☐ 3 ☐ 4 ☐ 5 ☐ 6 ☐ 7 ☐

8 ☐ 9 ☐ 10 ☐ 11 ☐ 12 ☐ 13 ☐ 14 ☐ 15 ☐ 16 ☐ 17 ☐ 18 ☐

Match results _____ Gross score _____ Nett score _____

Memories _____

_____

_____

_____

_____

_____

One of golf's earliest heroes, Tom Morris of St Andrews.

Tom Morris, St. Andrews

Score Card/Press Clippings/Notes

Round Reports

Course / Club _____ Date _____

Type of course (Links, etc.) _____

Length from medal tees _____ Club tees _____ Ladies tees _____

PAR _____ Standard scratch score (S.S.S.) _____

Weather conditions _____

_____

Course conditions: tees _____ fairways _____ rough _____

bunkers _____ greens _____

Overall observations _____

_____

_____

Player/s 1 _____ handicap _____

2 _____ handicap _____

3 _____ handicap _____

4 _____ handicap _____

Method of play: match / medal / Stableford / other _____

Stroke analysis

1 ☐ 2 ☐ 3 ☐ 4 ☐ 5 ☐ 6 ☐ 7 ☐ 8 ☐ 9 ☐

Score at the turn ☐

10 ☐ 11 ☐ 12 ☐ 13 ☐ 14 ☐ 15 ☐ 16 ☐ 17 ☐ 18 ☐

total ☐

Putting analysis (putts per hole) 1 ☐ 2 ☐ 3 ☐ 4 ☐ 5 ☐ 6 ☐ 7 ☐

8 ☐ 9 ☐ 10 ☐ 11 ☐ 12 ☐ 13 ☐ 14 ☐ 15 ☐ 16 ☐ 17 ☐ 18 ☐

Match results _____ Gross score _____ Nett score _____

Memories _____

_____

_____

_____

_____

_____

Round Reports

Course / Club _____ Date _____

Type of course (Links, etc.) _____

Length from medal tees _____ Club tees _____ Ladies tees _____

PAR _____ Standard scratch score (S.S.S.) _____

Weather conditions _____

_____

Course conditions: tees _____ fairways _____ rough _____

bunkers _____ greens _____

Overall observations _____

_____

_____

Player/s 1 _____ handicap _____

        2 _____ handicap _____

        3 _____ handicap _____

        4 _____ handicap _____

Method of play: match / medal / Stableford / other _____

Stroke analysis

      1 ☐ 2 ☐ 3 ☐ 4 ☐ 5 ☐ 6 ☐ 7 ☐ 8 ☐ 9 ☐

                        Score at the turn ☐

    10 ☐ 11 ☐ 12 ☐ 13 ☐ 14 ☐ 15 ☐ 16 ☐ 17 ☐ 18 ☐

                              total ☐

Putting analysis (putts per hole) 1 ☐ 2 ☐ 3 ☐ 4 ☐ 5 ☐ 6 ☐ 7 ☐

8 ☐ 9 ☐ 10 ☐ 11 ☐ 12 ☐ 13 ☐ 14 ☐ 15 ☐ 16 ☐ 17 ☐ 18 ☐

Match results _____ Gross score _____ Nett score _____

Memories _____

_____

_____

_____

_____

_____

CHURCHMAN'S CIGARETTES.

ABE MITCHELL.

CHURCHMAN'S CIGARETTES.

ROGER WETHERED.

CHURCHMAN'S CIGARETTES.

R. T. ("BOBBY") JONES.

CHURCHMAN'S CIGARETTES.

WALTER HAGEN.

Round Reports

Course / Club _____ Date _____

Type of course (Links, etc.) _____

Length from medal tees _____ Club tees _____ Ladies tees _____

PAR _____ Standard scratch score (S.S.S.) _____

Weather conditions _____

_____

Course conditions: tees _____ fairways _____ rough _____

bunkers _____ greens _____

Overall observations _____

_____

Player/s 1 _____ handicap _____

2 _____ handicap _____

3 _____ handicap _____

4 _____ handicap _____

Method of play: match / medal / Stableford / other _____

Stroke analysis

1 ☐ 2 ☐ 3 ☐ 4 ☐ 5 ☐ 6 ☐ 7 ☐ 8 ☐ 9 ☐

Score at the turn ☐

10 ☐ 11 ☐ 12 ☐ 13 ☐ 14 ☐ 15 ☐ 16 ☐ 17 ☐ 18 ☐

total ☐

Putting analysis (putts per hole) 1 ☐ 2 ☐ 3 ☐ 4 ☐ 5 ☐ 6 ☐ 7 ☐

8 ☐ 9 ☐ 10 ☐ 11 ☐ 12 ☐ 13 ☐ 14 ☐ 15 ☐ 16 ☐ 17 ☐ 18 ☐

Match results _____ Gross score _____ Nett score _____

Memories _____

_____

_____

_____

_____

_____

Score Card/Press Clippings/Notes

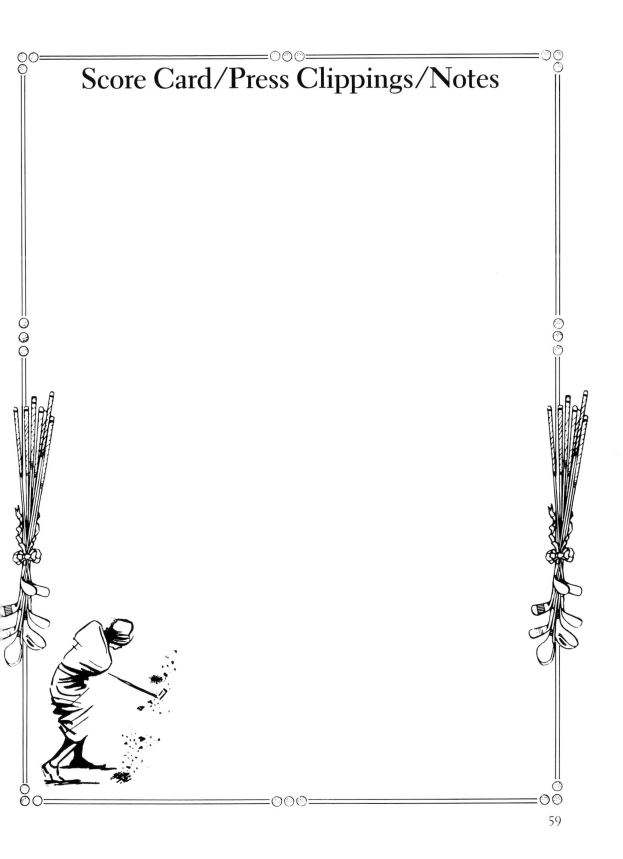

Course / Club _____ Date _____

Type of course (Links, etc.) _____

Length from medal tees _____ Club tees _____ Ladies tees _____

PAR _____ Standard scratch score (S.S.S.) _____

Weather conditions _____

_____

Course conditions: tees _____ fairways _____ rough _____

bunkers _____ greens _____

Overall observations _____

_____

_____

Player/s 1 _____ handicap _____

2 _____ handicap _____

3 _____ handicap _____

4 _____ handicap _____

Method of play: match / medal / Stableford / other _____

Stroke analysis

1 ☐ 2 ☐ 3 ☐ 4 ☐ 5 ☐ 6 ☐ 7 ☐ 8 ☐ 9 ☐

Score at the turn ☐

10 ☐ 11 ☐ 12 ☐ 13 ☐ 14 ☐ 15 ☐ 16 ☐ 17 ☐ 18 ☐

total ☐

Putting analysis (putts per hole) 1 ☐ 2 ☐ 3 ☐ 4 ☐ 5 ☐ 6 ☐ 7 ☐

8 ☐ 9 ☐ 10 ☐ 11 ☐ 12 ☐ 13 ☐ 14 ☐ 15 ☐ 16 ☐ 17 ☐ 18 ☐

Match results _____ Gross score _____ Nett score _____

Memories _____

_____

_____

_____

_____

_____

Score Card/Press Clippings/Notes

Round Reports

Course / Club _____ Date _____

Type of course (Links, etc.) _____

Length from medal tees _____ Club tees _____ Ladies tees _____

PAR _____ Standard scratch score (S.S.S.) _____

Weather conditions _____

_____

Course conditions: tees _____ fairways _____ rough _____

bunkers _____ greens _____

Overall observations _____

_____

_____

Player/s 1 _____ handicap _____

2 _____ handicap _____

3 _____ handicap _____

4 _____ handicap _____

Method of play: match / medal / Stableford / other _____

Stroke analysis

1 ☐ 2 ☐ 3 ☐ 4 ☐ 5 ☐ 6 ☐ 7 ☐ 8 ☐ 9 ☐

Score at the turn ☐

10 ☐ 11 ☐ 12 ☐ 13 ☐ 14 ☐ 15 ☐ 16 ☐ 17 ☐ 18 ☐

total ☐

Putting analysis (putts per hole) 1 ☐ 2 ☐ 3 ☐ 4 ☐ 5 ☐ 6 ☐ 7 ☐

8 ☐ 9 ☐ 10 ☐ 11 ☐ 12 ☐ 13 ☐ 14 ☐ 15 ☐ 16 ☐ 17 ☐ 18 ☐

Match results _____ Gross score _____ Nett score _____

Memories _____

_____

_____

_____

_____

_____

Round Reports

Course / Club _____ Date _____

Type of course (Links, etc.) _____

Length from medal tees _____ Club tees _____ Ladies tees _____

PAR _____ Standard scratch score (S.S.S.) _____

Weather conditions _____

_____

Course conditions: tees _____ fairways _____ rough _____

bunkers _____ greens _____

Overall observations _____

_____

_____

Player/s 1 _____ handicap _____

          2 _____ handicap _____

          3 _____ handicap _____

          4 _____ handicap _____

Method of play: match / medal / Stableford / other _____

Stroke analysis

     1 ☐ 2 ☐ 3 ☐ 4 ☐ 5 ☐ 6 ☐ 7 ☐ 8 ☐ 9 ☐

                  Score at the turn ☐

   10 ☐ 11 ☐ 12 ☐ 13 ☐ 14 ☐ 15 ☐ 16 ☐ 17 ☐ 18 ☐

                         total ☐

Putting analysis (putts per hole) 1 ☐ 2 ☐ 3 ☐ 4 ☐ 5 ☐ 6 ☐ 7 ☐

8 ☐ 9 ☐ 10 ☐ 11 ☐ 12 ☐ 13 ☐ 14 ☐ 15 ☐ 16 ☐ 17 ☐ 18 ☐

Match results _____ Gross score _____ Nett score _____

Memories _____

_____

_____

_____

_____

_____

Hints on Golf

By
Horace
Hutchinson

1/-

Round Reports

Course / Club _____ Date _____

Type of course (Links, etc.) _____

Length from medal tees _____ Club tees _____ Ladies tees _____

PAR _____ Standard scratch score (S.S.S.) _____

Weather conditions _____

_____

Course conditions: tees _____ fairways _____ rough _____

bunkers _____ greens _____

Overall observations _____

_____

Player/s 1 _____ handicap _____

2 _____ handicap _____

3 _____ handicap _____

4 _____ handicap _____

Method of play: match / medal / Stableford / other _____

Stroke analysis

1 ☐ 2 ☐ 3 ☐ 4 ☐ 5 ☐ 6 ☐ 7 ☐ 8 ☐ 9 ☐

Score at the turn ☐

10 ☐ 11 ☐ 12 ☐ 13 ☐ 14 ☐ 15 ☐ 16 ☐ 17 ☐ 18 ☐

total ☐

Putting analysis (putts per hole) 1 ☐ 2 ☐ 3 ☐ 4 ☐ 5 ☐ 6 ☐ 7 ☐

8 ☐ 9 ☐ 10 ☐ 11 ☐ 12 ☐ 13 ☐ 14 ☐ 15 ☐ 16 ☐ 17 ☐ 18 ☐

Match results _____ Gross score _____ Nett score _____

Memories _____

_____

_____

_____

_____

_____

Score Card/Press Clippings/Notes

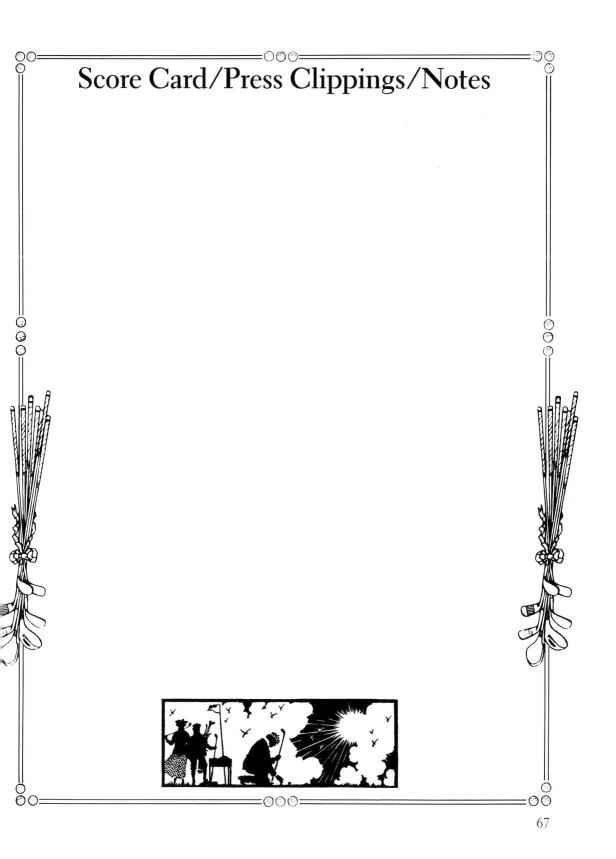

Round Reports

Course / Club _____ Date _____

Type of course (Links, etc.) _____

Length from medal tees _____ Club tees _____ Ladies tees _____

PAR _____ Standard scratch score (S.S.S.) _____

Weather conditions _____

_____

Course conditions: tees _____ fairways _____ rough _____

bunkers _____ greens _____

Overall observations _____

_____

_____

Player/s 1 _____ handicap _____

2 _____ handicap _____

3 _____ handicap _____

4 _____ handicap _____

Method of play: match / medal / Stableford / other _____

Stroke analysis

1 ☐ 2 ☐ 3 ☐ 4 ☐ 5 ☐ 6 ☐ 7 ☐ 8 ☐ 9 ☐

Score at the turn ☐

10 ☐ 11 ☐ 12 ☐ 13 ☐ 14 ☐ 15 ☐ 16 ☐ 17 ☐ 18 ☐

total ☐

Putting analysis (putts per hole) 1 ☐ 2 ☐ 3 ☐ 4 ☐ 5 ☐ 6 ☐ 7 ☐

8 ☐ 9 ☐ 10 ☐ 11 ☐ 12 ☐ 13 ☐ 14 ☐ 15 ☐ 16 ☐ 17 ☐ 18 ☐

Match results _____ Gross score _____ Nett score _____

Memories _____

_____

_____

_____

_____

_____

Frank Reynolds at Sunningdale for the News of the World, later Matchplay, Championship 1903.

The famous 17th hole

E. Ray, runner-up

James Braid driving

T. Williamson judges an approach

Braid and that Niblick

The Open Champion on the green

An innovation

F R

Score Card/Press Clippings/Notes

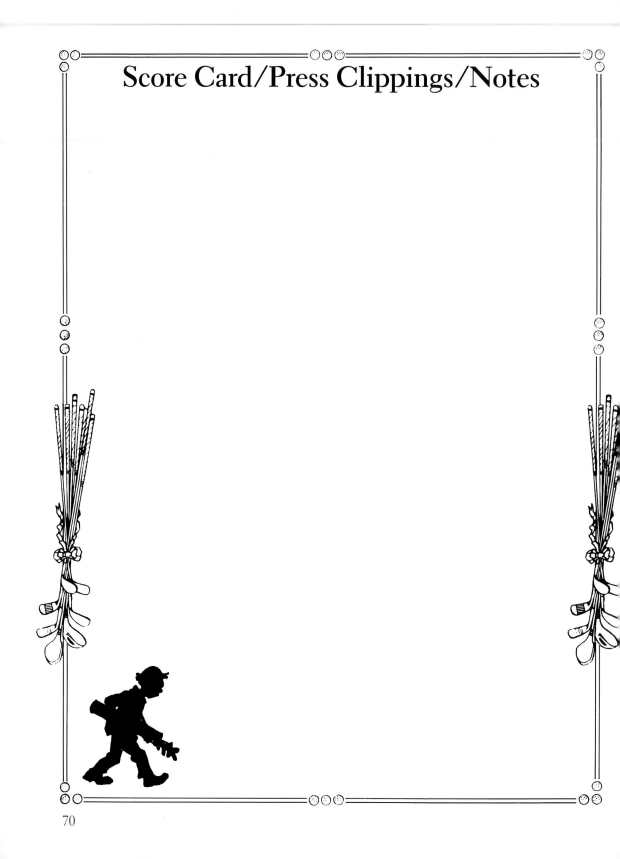

Round Reports

Course / Club _____ Date _____

Type of course (Links, etc.) _____

Length from medal tees _____ Club tees _____ Ladies tees _____

PAR _____ Standard scratch score (S.S.S.) _____

Weather conditions _____

_____

Course conditions: tees _____ fairways _____ rough _____

bunkers _____ greens _____

Overall observations _____

_____

_____

Player/s 1 _____ handicap _____

2 _____ handicap _____

3 _____ handicap _____

4 _____ handicap _____

Method of play: match / medal / Stableford / other _____

Stroke analysis

1 ☐ 2 ☐ 3 ☐ 4 ☐ 5 ☐ 6 ☐ 7 ☐ 8 ☐ 9 ☐

Score at the turn ☐

10 ☐ 11 ☐ 12 ☐ 13 ☐ 14 ☐ 15 ☐ 16 ☐ 17 ☐ 18 ☐

total ☐

Putting analysis (putts per hole) 1 ☐ 2 ☐ 3 ☐ 4 ☐ 5 ☐ 6 ☐ 7 ☐

8 ☐ 9 ☐ 10 ☐ 11 ☐ 12 ☐ 13 ☐ 14 ☐ 15 ☐ 16 ☐ 17 ☐ 18 ☐

Match results _____ Gross score _____ Nett score _____

Memories _____

_____

_____

_____

_____

_____

Round Reports

Course / Club _____ Date _____

Type of course (Links, etc.) _____

Length from medal tees _____ Club tees _____ Ladies tees _____

PAR _____ Standard scratch score (S.S.S.) _____

Weather conditions _____

_____

Course conditions: tees _____ fairways _____ rough _____

bunkers _____ greens _____

Overall observations _____

_____

_____

Player/s 1 _____ handicap _____

2 _____ handicap _____

3 _____ handicap _____

4 _____ handicap _____

Method of play: match / medal / Stableford / other _____

Stroke analysis

1 ☐ 2 ☐ 3 ☐ 4 ☐ 5 ☐ 6 ☐ 7 ☐ 8 ☐ 9 ☐

Score at the turn ☐

10 ☐ 11 ☐ 12 ☐ 13 ☐ 14 ☐ 15 ☐ 16 ☐ 17 ☐ 18 ☐

total ☐

Putting analysis (putts per hole) 1 ☐ 2 ☐ 3 ☐ 4 ☐ 5 ☐ 6 ☐ 7 ☐

8 ☐ 9 ☐ 10 ☐ 11 ☐ 12 ☐ 13 ☐ 14 ☐ 15 ☐ 16 ☐ 17 ☐ 18 ☐

Match results _____ Gross score _____ Nett score _____

Memories _____

_____

_____

_____

_____

_____

Wills's cigarette cards.

WILL'S CIGARETTES.

MISS CECIL LEITCH.

WILL'S CIGARETTES.

J. H. TAYLOR.

WILL'S CIGARETTES.

MISS JOYCE WETHERED.

WILL'S CIGARETTES.

WALTER J. HAGEN.

Round Reports

Course / Club _____ Date _____

Type of course (Links, etc.) _____

Length from medal tees _____ Club tees _____ Ladies tees _____

PAR _____ Standard scratch score (S.S.S.) _____

Weather conditions _____

_____

Course conditions: tees _____ fairways _____ rough _____

bunkers _____ greens _____

Overall observations _____

_____

_____

Player/s 1 _____ handicap _____

2 _____ handicap _____

3 _____ handicap _____

4 _____ handicap _____

Method of play: match / medal / Stableford / other _____

Stroke analysis

1 ☐ 2 ☐ 3 ☐ 4 ☐ 5 ☐ 6 ☐ 7 ☐ 8 ☐ 9 ☐

Score at the turn ☐

10 ☐ 11 ☐ 12 ☐ 13 ☐ 14 ☐ 15 ☐ 16 ☐ 17 ☐ 18 ☐

total ☐

Putting analysis (putts per hole) 1 ☐ 2 ☐ 3 ☐ 4 ☐ 5 ☐ 6 ☐ 7 ☐

8 ☐ 9 ☐ 10 ☐ 11 ☐ 12 ☐ 13 ☐ 14 ☐ 15 ☐ 16 ☐ 17 ☐ 18 ☐

Match results _____ Gross score _____ Nett score _____

Memories _____

_____

_____

_____

_____

_____

Score Card/Press Clippings/Notes

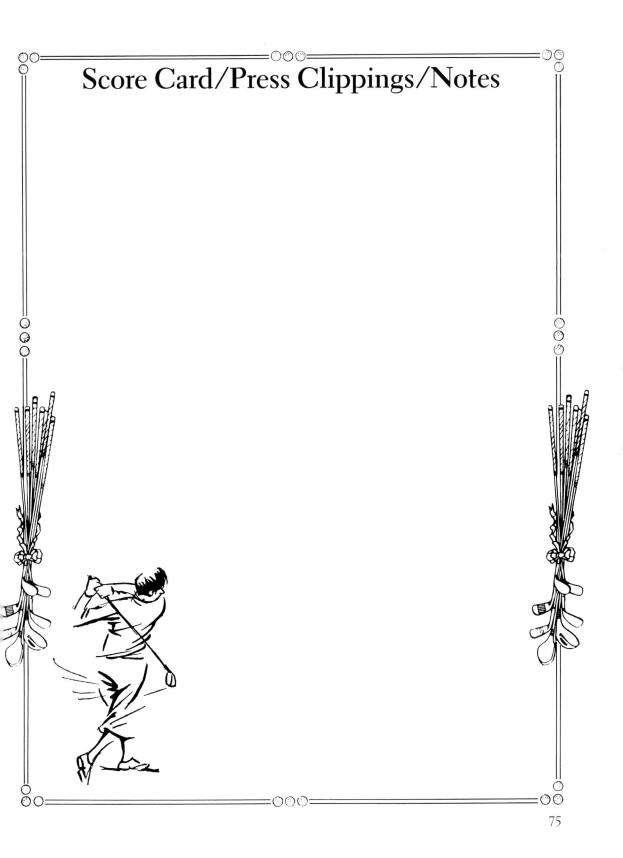

Course / Club _____ Date _____

Type of course (Links, etc.) _____

Length from medal tees _____ Club tees _____ Ladies tees _____

PAR _____ Standard scratch score (S.S.S.) _____

Weather conditions _____

_____

Course conditions: tees _____ fairways _____ rough _____

bunkers _____ greens _____

Overall observations _____

_____

_____

Player/s 1 _____ handicap _____

2 _____ handicap _____

3 _____ handicap _____

4 _____ handicap _____

Method of play: match / medal / Stableford / other _____

Stroke analysis

1 ☐ 2 ☐ 3 ☐ 4 ☐ 5 ☐ 6 ☐ 7 ☐ 8 ☐ 9 ☐

Score at the turn ☐

10 ☐ 11 ☐ 12 ☐ 13 ☐ 14 ☐ 15 ☐ 16 ☐ 17 ☐ 18 ☐

total ☐

Putting analysis (putts per hole) 1 ☐ 2 ☐ 3 ☐ 4 ☐ 5 ☐ 6 ☐ 7 ☐

8 ☐ 9 ☐ 10 ☐ 11 ☐ 12 ☐ 13 ☐ 14 ☐ 15 ☐ 16 ☐ 17 ☐ 18 ☐

Match results _____ Gross score _____ Nett score _____

Memories _____

_____

_____

_____

_____

_____

A French view of the beauties of golf.

Score Card/Press Clippings/Notes

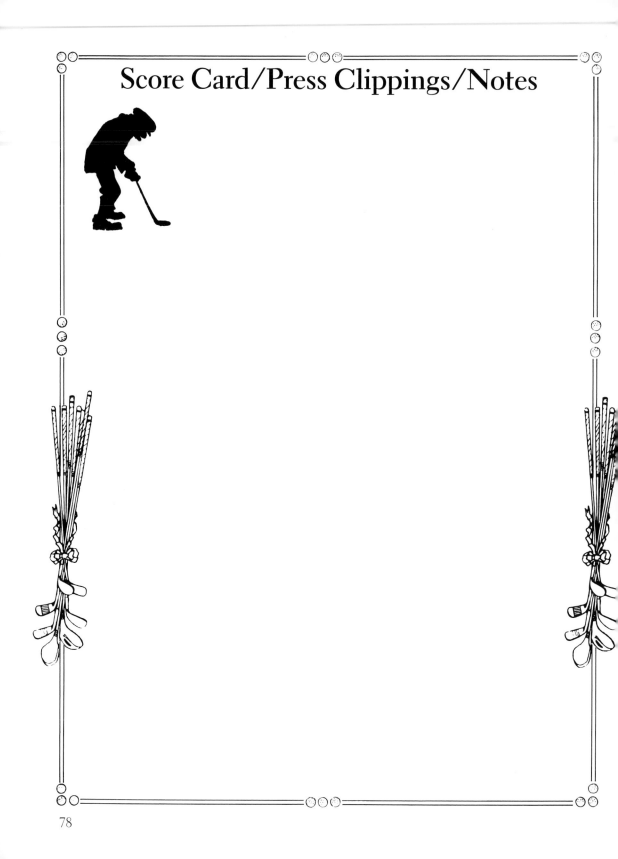

Round Reports

Course / Club _____ Date _____

Type of course (Links, etc.) _____

Length from medal tees _____ Club tees _____ Ladies tees _____

PAR _____ Standard scratch score (S.S.S.) _____

Weather conditions _____

_____

Course conditions: tees _____ fairways _____ rough _____

bunkers _____ greens _____

Overall observations _____

_____

_____

Player/s 1 _____ handicap _____

2 _____ handicap _____

3 _____ handicap _____

4 _____ handicap _____

Method of play: match / medal / Stableford / other _____

Stroke analysis

1 ☐ 2 ☐ 3 ☐ 4 ☐ 5 ☐ 6 ☐ 7 ☐ 8 ☐ 9 ☐

Score at the turn ☐

10 ☐ 11 ☐ 12 ☐ 13 ☐ 14 ☐ 15 ☐ 16 ☐ 17 ☐ 18 ☐

total ☐

Putting analysis (putts per hole) 1 ☐ 2 ☐ 3 ☐ 4 ☐ 5 ☐ 6 ☐ 7 ☐

8 ☐ 9 ☐ 10 ☐ 11 ☐ 12 ☐ 13 ☐ 14 ☐ 15 ☐ 16 ☐ 17 ☐ 18 ☐

Match results _____ Gross score _____ Nett score _____

Memories _____

_____

_____

_____

_____

_____

Round Reports

Course / Club _____ Date _____

Type of course (Links, etc.) _____

Length from medal tees _____ Club tees _____ Ladies tees _____

PAR _____ Standard scratch score (S.S.S.) _____

Weather conditions _____

_____

Course conditions: tees _____ fairways _____ rough _____

bunkers _____ greens _____

Overall observations _____

_____

_____

Player/s 1 _____ handicap _____

2 _____ handicap _____

3 _____ handicap _____

4 _____ handicap _____

Method of play: match / medal / Stableford / other _____

Stroke analysis

1 ☐ 2 ☐ 3 ☐ 4 ☐ 5 ☐ 6 ☐ 7 ☐ 8 ☐ 9 ☐

Score at the turn ☐

10 ☐ 11 ☐ 12 ☐ 13 ☐ 14 ☐ 15 ☐ 16 ☐ 17 ☐ 18 ☐

total ☐

Putting analysis (putts per hole) 1 ☐ 2 ☐ 3 ☐ 4 ☐ 5 ☐ 6 ☐ 7 ☐

8 ☐ 9 ☐ 10 ☐ 11 ☐ 12 ☐ 13 ☐ 14 ☐ 15 ☐ 16 ☐ 17 ☐ 18 ☐

Match results _____ Gross score _____ Nett score _____

Memories _____

_____

_____

_____

_____

_____

Golfing motifs adorn John Henry Taylor's book.

Round Reports

Course / Club _____ Date _____

Type of course (Links, etc.) _____

Length from medal tees _____ Club tees _____ Ladies tees _____

PAR _____ Standard scratch score (S.S.S.) _____

Weather conditions _____

_____

Course conditions: tees _____ fairways _____ rough _____

bunkers _____ greens _____

Overall observations _____

_____

_____

Player/s 1 _____ handicap _____

2 _____ handicap _____

3 _____ handicap _____

4 _____ handicap _____

Method of play: match / medal / Stableford / other _____

Stroke analysis

1 ☐ 2 ☐ 3 ☐ 4 ☐ 5 ☐ 6 ☐ 7 ☐ 8 ☐ 9 ☐

Score at the turn ☐

10 ☐ 11 ☐ 12 ☐ 13 ☐ 14 ☐ 15 ☐ 16 ☐ 17 ☐ 18 ☐

total ☐

Putting analysis (putts per hole) 1 ☐ 2 ☐ 3 ☐ 4 ☐ 5 ☐ 6 ☐ 7 ☐

8 ☐ 9 ☐ 10 ☐ 11 ☐ 12 ☐ 13 ☐ 14 ☐ 15 ☐ 16 ☐ 17 ☐ 18 ☐

Match results _____ Gross score _____ Nett score _____

Memories _____

_____

_____

_____

_____

_____

Score Card/Press Clippings/Notes

Round Reports

Course / Club _____ Date _____

Type of course (Links, etc.) _____

Length from medal tees _____ Club tees _____ Ladies tees _____

PAR _____ Standard scratch score (S.S.S.) _____

Weather conditions _____

_____

Course conditions: tees _____ fairways _____ rough _____

bunkers _____ greens _____

Overall observations _____

_____

_____

Player/s 1 _____ handicap _____

2 _____ handicap _____

3 _____ handicap _____

4 _____ handicap _____

Method of play: match / medal / Stableford / other _____

Stroke analysis

1 ☐ 2 ☐ 3 ☐ 4 ☐ 5 ☐ 6 ☐ 7 ☐ 8 ☐ 9 ☐

Score at the turn ☐

10 ☐ 11 ☐ 12 ☐ 13 ☐ 14 ☐ 15 ☐ 16 ☐ 17 ☐ 18 ☐

total ☐

Putting analysis (putts per hole) 1 ☐ 2 ☐ 3 ☐ 4 ☐ 5 ☐ 6 ☐ 7 ☐

8 ☐ 9 ☐ 10 ☐ 11 ☐ 12 ☐ 13 ☐ 14 ☐ 15 ☐ 16 ☐ 17 ☐ 18 ☐

Match results _____ Gross score _____ Nett score _____

Memories _____

_____

_____

_____

_____

_____

John Henry Taylor amongst personalities featured on Copes cards.

8.—A. J. BALFOUR.
"Putting the most trying to
the Nerves."

12.—ALLAN ROBERTSON.

13.—Mr. CRAWFORD.
Caddie and Golf Professor.

22.—J. H. TAYLOR.
Open Champion 1894-5.

24.—HAROLD HILTON.

25.—J. BALL.
A Celebrated Golf Ball.

Score Card/Press Clippings/Notes

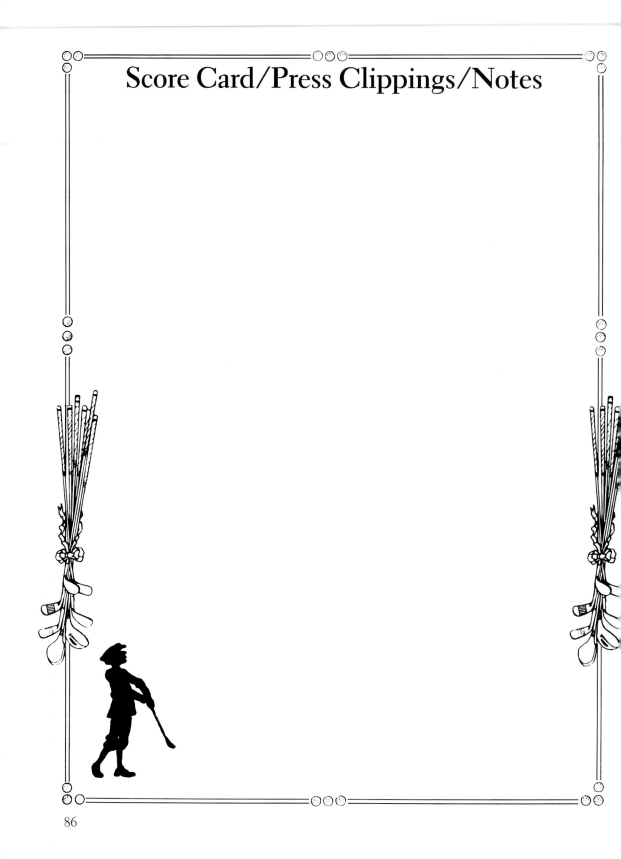

Round Reports

Course / Club _____ Date _____

Type of course (Links, etc.) _____

Length from medal tees _____ Club tees _____ Ladies tees _____

PAR _____ Standard scratch score (S.S.S.) _____

Weather conditions _____
_____

Course conditions: tees _____ fairways _____ rough _____

bunkers _____ greens _____

Overall observations _____
_____
_____

Player/s 1 _____ handicap _____
2 _____ handicap _____
3 _____ handicap _____
4 _____ handicap _____

Method of play: match / medal / Stableford / other _____

Stroke analysis

1 ☐ 2 ☐ 3 ☐ 4 ☐ 5 ☐ 6 ☐ 7 ☐ 8 ☐ 9 ☐

Score at the turn ☐

10 ☐ 11 ☐ 12 ☐ 13 ☐ 14 ☐ 15 ☐ 16 ☐ 17 ☐ 18 ☐

total ☐

Putting analysis (putts per hole) 1 ☐ 2 ☐ 3 ☐ 4 ☐ 5 ☐ 6 ☐ 7 ☐

8 ☐ 9 ☐ 10 ☐ 11 ☐ 12 ☐ 13 ☐ 14 ☐ 15 ☐ 16 ☐ 17 ☐ 18 ☐

Match results _____ Gross score _____ Nett score _____

Memories _____
_____
_____
_____
_____
_____

Round Reports

Course / Club _____ Date _____

Type of course (Links, etc.) _____

Length from medal tees _____ Club tees _____ Ladies tees _____

PAR _____ Standard scratch score (S.S.S.) _____

Weather conditions _____

_____

Course conditions: tees _____ fairways _____ rough _____

bunkers _____ greens _____

Overall observations _____

_____

Player/s 1 _____ handicap _____

2 _____ handicap _____

3 _____ handicap _____

4 _____ handicap _____

Method of play: match / medal / Stableford / other _____

Stroke analysis

1 ☐ 2 ☐ 3 ☐ 4 ☐ 5 ☐ 6 ☐ 7 ☐ 8 ☐ 9 ☐

Score at the turn ☐

10 ☐ 11 ☐ 12 ☐ 13 ☐ 14 ☐ 15 ☐ 16 ☐ 17 ☐ 18 ☐

total ☐

Putting analysis (putts per hole) 1 ☐ 2 ☐ 3 ☐ 4 ☐ 5 ☐ 6 ☐ 7 ☐

8 ☐ 9 ☐ 10 ☐ 11 ☐ 12 ☐ 13 ☐ 14 ☐ 15 ☐ 16 ☐ 17 ☐ 18 ☐

Match results _____ Gross score _____ Nett score _____

Memories _____

_____

_____

_____

_____

_____

'He's stopped beating it, Mummy, I think it must be dead!' – by Frank Reynolds.

Frank
Reynolds

Score Card/Press Clippings/Notes

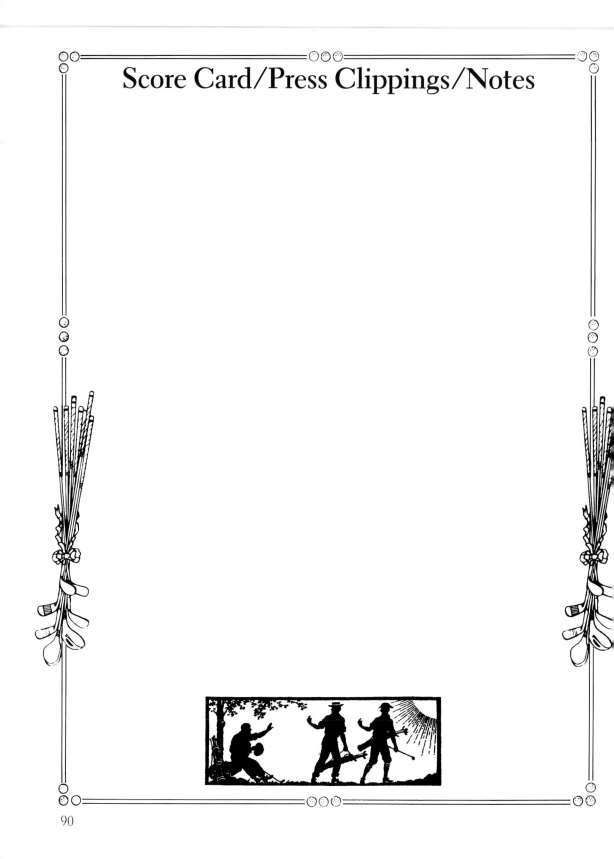

Course Reports

Course _____

Best holes _____

_____

Memories / comments _____

_____

_____

_____

_____

Course _____

Best holes _____

_____

Memories / comments _____

_____

_____

_____

_____

Course _____

Best holes _____

_____

Memories / comments _____

_____

_____

_____

_____

Course _____

Best Holes _____

_____

Memories / comments _____

_____

_____

Course Reports

Course _____
Best holes _____
_____

Memories / comments _____
_____
_____
_____
_____

Course _____
Best holes _____
_____

Memories / comments _____
_____
_____
_____
_____

Course _____
Best holes _____
_____

Memories / comments _____
_____
_____
_____
_____

Course _____
Best Holes _____
_____

Memories / comments _____
_____
_____
_____

Famous courses figured on Wills's cigarette cards.

WILL'S CIGARETTES.

WESTWARD HO!
Bunkers in front of 4th Tee.

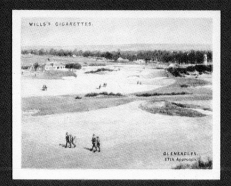

WILL'S CIGARETTES.

GLENEAGLES.
17th Approach.

WILL'S CIGARETTES.

TURNBERRY.
18th Green.

WILL'S CIGARETTES.

ST. ANDREWS.
The Club house.

WILL'S CIGARETTES.

MUIRFIELD.
18th Green.

WILL'S CIGARETTES.

TROON.
18th Green.

Course Reports

Course _____

Best holes _____

_____

Memories / comments _____

_____

_____

_____

Course _____

Best holes _____

_____

Memories / comments _____

_____

_____

_____

Course _____

Best holes _____

_____

Memories / comments _____

_____

_____

_____

Course _____

Best Holes _____

_____

Memories / comments _____

_____

_____

Course Reports

Course _____

Best holes _____

_____

Memories / comments _____

_____

_____

_____

_____

Course _____

Best holes _____

_____

Memories / comments _____

_____

_____

_____

_____

Course _____

Best holes _____

_____

Memories / comments _____

_____

_____

_____

_____

Course _____

Best Holes _____

_____

Memories / comments _____

_____

_____

Eclectic Score

	PAR	Eclectic score							
1									
2									
3									
4									
5									
6									
7									
8									
9									
10									
11									
12									
13									
14									
15									
16									
17									
18									
Total									

Notes

PARTICULARS OF GAMES PLAYED OVER STRANGE LINKS.

Place of Links	Worthing
Name of Secretary	
How to get there...	By train
Convenient { **there**...	
Trains · · { **back** ...	
Opponent's H'cap.	
Condition of Greens	Fast
Name of Professional	MacEwan
Remarks on Course **(Position of** **Bunkers, Water,** **Fog, etc., etc.)**	Very sporting new Course. Rather mountainous. One of the best Course of Sussex.